HAMLET

PRINCE OF DENMARK

Ransom

Hamlet, Prince of Denmark
Published by Ransom Publishing Ltd.
Unit 7, Brocklands Farm, West Meon, Hampshire GU32 1JN, UK
www.ransom.co.uk

ISBN   978 178591 335 8
First published in 2019

CONTENTS

WHERE

Denmark. A country in the northern part of Europe.

Most of the action takes place in Elsinore Castle, which is a real castle in Denmark.

"Elsinore Castle"

WHEN

The events in the play take place some time in the past, probably between about 1550 and 1600.

The play itself was written between 1599 and 1602.

WHO

Hamlet
– Prince of Denmark

Claudius – King of Denmark and Hamlet's uncle

Gertrude – Hamlet's mother and Claudius's wife

Claudius   Gertrude

Horatio – Hamlet's best friend

Polonius – Lord Chamberlain to the king

Ophelia – Polonius's daughter

Laertes – Polonius's son

Ophelia   Polonius   Laertes

Young Fortinbras – Prince of Norway

Rosencrantz)
Guildenstern) – two courtiers

Osric – a courtier

Marcellus)
Bernardo) – two officers

Reynaldo – Polonius's servant

HELPFUL NOTE

All the spoken words in this book that are in italics, *'like this'*, are actual words taken from Shakespeare's play. They are spoken by one of the actors in the play.

The Ghost – the spirit of Hamlet's father, who was King of Denmark before his death

The Ghost

The Globe Theatre. Above is a reconstruction of the original Globe Theatre, which is in London. Below is a cross-section of the original theatre, which was built in 1599.

Shakespeare's plays were performed at this theatre. When you read this book, just imagine standing in the crowd, in front of this stage, watching the play.

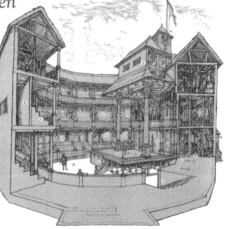

ONE

It's night, and **Bernardo** stands guard outside Elsinore Castle. He is joined by **Marcellus**, an officer (or sentry), and **Horatio**, who was a good friend of the now-dead King Hamlet, King of Denmark.

Horatio has heard people talking about a ghost walking the castle at night, and now he has come to see for himself.

As they stand there, **the ghost** of the dead King Hamlet comes out of the freezing fog and rain, towards the three men.

They stand there, paralysed with fear. The cold seems to go through their armour

until it touches their hearts. Marcellus and
Barnardo are strong men, and Horatio
knew the old king well. Yet all three are
sick with fear.

Horatio speaks to the ghost. '*What art
thou that usurp'st this time of night …*

by heaven I charge thee, speak!'

But, as Horatio speaks, the ghost moves
away and disappears.

The three men look at each other. Why
did the ghost appear to them? Horatio
thinks he knows the answer. Old King

Hamlet defeated the old King of Norway. Now his son, **Young Fortinbras**, Prince of Norway, is seeking to get back land lost by his father. *This*, says Horatio, is why the ghost of old King Hamlet cannot rest.

Then suddenly the ghost reappears. It spreads its arms and, just as a cock crows, it disappears again.

'We have to tell **Prince Hamlet**,' says Horatio, 'that his father is not at rest.'

Within the castle, things are moving on since old King Hamlet's death. The old king's brother, **Claudius**, has been made king, and Claudius has married old King Hamlet's wife, **Gertrude**. So Prince Hamlet has a new step-dad.

But Hamlet feels no affection for his new step-father – and he's still mourning the loss of his father. What's worse, his mother has no sympathy: *'Thou know'st 'tis common; all that lives must die,'* she says. Some help that is!

Claudius even accuses Prince Hamlet of mourning out of sheer stubbornness!

As everybody leaves, Hamlet is alone to give us his true thoughts. His father was a great king, he says, but Claudius is an old goat ('*satyr*') compared to him. And as for his mother, Gertrude, well she married Claudius within just a month of old King Hamlet's death. A month!

'*O God! God!*
How weary, stale, flat, and unprofitable,
Seem to me all the uses of this world!'

So Prince Hamlet's feeling pretty fed up, all things considered.

Then Horatio turns up, introducing himself to Hamlet as '*your poor servant ever*'.

'My friend, not my servant,' says Hamlet. (At this moment, Hamlet needs friends.)

'Why aren't you at University in Wittenberg?' Hamlet asks Horatio. (Both Hamlet and Horatio are students there.)

'I came for your father's funeral, my lord,' Horatio tells him.

'Don't mock me,' says Hamlet. 'I think you came to see my mother's wedding.'

'Well, my lord, one was very soon after the other.'

'You can save money like that, Horatio. The leftovers from the funeral dinner made a great cold lunch for the wedding!' (Ouch!)

Hamlet talks to Horatio about how great his father was.

'*I shall not look upon his like again.*'

'Funny you should say that,' thinks Horatio. '*My lord, I think I saw him yesternight.*'

Well, that's a conversation-stopper!

So Horatio tells Hamlet what he and the two guards had seen, and how the ghost had been wearing full battle armour.

'Did he look mad?' Hamlet asks.

'*A countenance more in sorrow than in anger,*' replies Horatio.

Hamlet decides that he will join them tonight, in the hope that he too will see the ghost of his father. He asks Horatio and the guards to tell no one.

'My *father's spirit in arms! all is not well*,' he says.

Meanwhile, **Laertes** and his sister **Ophelia** are at home. Laertes is saying his farewells to Ophelia. He is making a trip back to France, and he is ready to go.

But before he leaves, he warns Ophelia about young Prince Hamlet. Ophelia is young, innocent and beautiful, and Laertes knows what young men are like! He tells his sister that she must keep Hamlet at arm's length until she is sure he means to marry her. Even then, even if Hamlet really loves her, he may still become king – and as king he may not be able to choose his own wife. Ophelia must not give in to him and then find herself dumped for a new queen. Nobody would want the king's ex!

Poor Ophelia! She also has a very chatty,

self-important father, **Polonius**, who is the king's Lord Chamberlain.

'What was Laertes just saying to you?' Polonius asks her. He has to know everything!

So Ophelia tells her father what Laertes said to her. Polonius has noticed Hamlet spending a lot of time with his daughter, and he's not happy about it.

'But the Lord Hamlet says he loves me,' Ophelia says.

'When the blood is burning, the tongue makes promises easily,' replies Polonius. 'Do you believe him?'

'*I do not know, my lord, what I should think,*' replies Ophelia.

The conversation doesn't go well. Polonius ends up ordering his daughter to stay away from Hamlet completely.

'*I shall obey, my lord,*' she says wearily. But she is deeply in love with the young prince. Surely he wouldn't lie to her?

At midnight, Hamlet, Horatio and Marcellus wait on the battlements. Below, in the castle, they can hear Claudius and the Danish court: loud, shouting and very drunk.

As they watch, the ghost appears before them. It beckons Hamlet away from the others and, even though the others try to stop him, Hamlet follows the ghost.

When the two of them are alone, the ghost speaks to Hamlet:

'I am thy father's spirit,

Doom'd for a certain term to walk the night,

And for the day confined to fast in fires,

Till the foul crimes done in my days of nature

Are burnt and purged away.'

Then the ghost tells Hamlet the awful truth: Hamlet's father was murdered. It was *'Murder most foul.'*

The ghost continues. 'The official story is that a poisonous snake bit me and I died. But that's not true. *But know, thou noble youth,*

*The serpent that did sting thy father's life
Now wears his crown.'*

'Claudius? My uncle Claudius killed the old king?'

'I was sleeping in the orchard when I was murdered. The murderer crept up like a coward and poured poison in my ear that curdled my blood like smelly rotten milk and caused a scab to form all over my body. I lost my life, my crown and my queen!

'Because I was suddenly murdered, I did not have time to confess and make amends for the things I had done wrong in life. So now I am only allowed to walk free for these few hours of darkness. The rest of the time, I am tortured in the fires of Hell, until the things I did wrong burn away!'

The ghost asks Hamlet to take revenge on Claudius, but tells him that he should not take revenge on his mother, Gertrude. Rather, he should leave her fate to God and the sting of her own guilt.

Then the ghost disappears.

As Hamlet stands there, Horatio and Marcellus catch up with him.

Hamlet does not tell them about the conversation he had with the ghost. He simply asks his friends to swear that they will '*Never make known what you have seen to-night.*'

They say they can be trusted to keep silent; they do not need to swear it.

'*Swear!*' the ghost's voice booms out. '*Swear!*'

'This is all very strange,' says Horatio.

'*And therefore as a stranger give it welcome.*

There are more things in heaven and earth,
Horatio,

Than are dreamt of in your philosophy,'
replies Hamlet.

In other words, you don't need to understand. Just swear.

Then Hamlet tells them that, no matter how strangely he behaves in future (and he may be forced to act as if he were mad, or, as he says, '*put an antic disposition on*'), they must never *ever* speak of what they saw tonight.

Of course they swear. They love Hamlet and would do anything for him.

Now Hamlet knows what he must do. He must kill Claudius. As they leave, he tells the others:

'*The time is out of joint: O cursed spite,*
That ever I was born to set it right!'

TWO

Over at Polonius's house, Polonius is sneakily arranging to send a servant, **Reynaldo,** to spy on his son Laertes, who is still in France. Polonius doesn't want to spend good money on Laertes if he's just over there having a good time!

Just as Reynaldo leaves, Ophelia rushes in with a story about how strangely Hamlet is acting. His clothes are dishevelled and he has a look 'As if he had been loosed out of hell.'

Ophelia says she has been avoiding Hamlet and sending his letters back unopened, just as she promised her father she would. So what is going on?

'Aha!' Polonius thinks, *'This is the very ecstasy of love.'* Hamlet is being driven mad by his love for Ophelia. 'Perhaps I was wrong!' thinks Polonius. 'Perhaps he really loves my daughter after all! I must tell King Claudius. Keeping it secret might cause more sadness.'

Back at the castle, King Claudius and Queen Gertrude are attending to state business. First, they greet two courtiers, **Rosencrantz** and **Guildenstern**.

Claudius tells them he is concerned about recent changes in Hamlet's behaviour. Since they are old school friends of Hamlet, can they spend some time with him and find out the reason for these changes?

Polonius then turns up and announces to King Claudius that he has found *'The very cause of Hamlet's lunacy.'*

But first there is a message from the ambassadors, who have just returned from Norway. As Polonius says, 'My *news shall be the fruit* [dessert] *to that great feast.*'

It turns out that the King of Norway's son, young Prince Fortinbras, was leading some rebels against Claudius, but then the King of Norway found out and gave Fortinbras money to attack the Poles instead. All that is needed now is for Claudius to give Fortinbras permission to cross Denmark on the way to fight the Poles.

Claudius says he will think about it.

Then Polonius tells the king and queen why Prince Hamlet is so moody.

'Your noble son is mad: mad I call it, but it's difficult to say what "mad" is. It would be mad to try to do it! That he is mad is true. It's a pity it's true. It's true it's a pity.'

Polonius talks a lot.

'Get on with it!' Gertrude tells him.

Finally Polonius gets to the point: Hamlet

is madly in love with Ophelia – and Polonius
has a letter to prove it! And because Polonius
banned his daughter from seeing or writing
to Hamlet, that's why Hamlet fell *'Into the
madness wherein now he raves.'*

Polonius suggests that they test his
theory. He will get Ophelia to meet Hamlet
alone – just the two of them – except that
Polonius and Claudius will watch them in
secret. That way, they'll be able to see
whether Hamlet really loves Ophelia.

At that very moment, just as they are all
listening to Polonius describe his plan,
Hamlet walks in.

'Do you know me, my lord?' asks Polonius.

'You are a fishmonger,' answers Hamlet.

They carry on talking. Hamlet seems to
be completely mad – but is he really?
Sometimes he speaks with great clarity. As
Polonius says, *'Though this be madness, yet
there is method in't.'*

Could Hamlet be faking madness?

Rosencrantz and Guildenstern meet with
Hamlet, to try to find out why he is so sad,
but he just winds them up and laughs at
them. Hamlet knows that they are spying
for Claudius – and he manages to get them
to admit it.

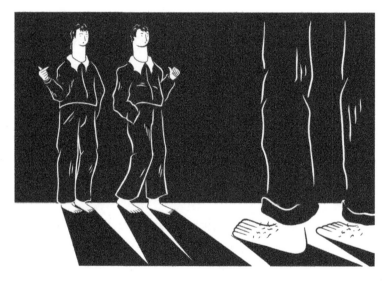

Rosencrantz announces that some actors
are on their way to entertain Hamlet.
(Hamlet has seen the actors before and he
loved watching them).

It's clear that Hamlet still has his wits

about him. Talking of the actors, he says, *'He that plays the king shall be welcome.'* (Just as Claudius is not the real king, but an actor, an imposter, playing the part.)

Suddenly a trumpet sounds and the actors arrive. There is shouting and laughter.

Hamlet gives a clue to Guildenstern. He tells him that he is deceiving the king and queen, because he is only mad at certain times. At other times, he knows exactly what is happening:

'I am but mad north-north-west: when the wind is southerly, I know a hawk from a handsaw.'

Then Hamlet begin to tell the story about the Trojan Horse, in the time of the Ancient Greeks. It is a story about how King Pyrrhus got revenge against Priam, the King of Troy. (It's a story that Shakespeare's audiences would have known well, and it is also a story about seeking revenge against a king.)

As Polonius takes the actors to their

rooms, Hamlet is left alone to think about things.

He has made a promise to the ghost of his father that he will kill Claudius. But even so, he needs to be certain that Claudius is guilty. The ghost might not have been the ghost of his father; it could just have been the devil in a 'pleasing shape'.

Hamlet decides that he will get the actors to act out a play with events similar to those of his father's death. He will watch Claudius's face, and then he will know the truth.

'The play's the thing
Wherein I'll catch the conscience of the king.'

THREE

Inside the castle, Rosenkrantz and Guildenstern are reporting to King Claudius and Gertrude. They tell Claudius that Hamlet wants them all to watch the actors' play with him, later that night. Claudius and Gertrude happily agree to attend.

Then Polonius's plan is put into effect. Ophelia sits and waits for Hamlet, while Polonius and Claudius hide. (Ophelia knows all about her father's plan.)

Hamlet enters. He is thinking aloud.

'To be, or not to be: that is the question:
Whether 'tis nobler in the mind to suffer
The slings and arrows of outrageous fortune,
Or to take arms against a sea of troubles,
And by opposing end them?'

Hamlet is thinking of suicide. Everything is so difficult. Is it all really worth the struggle? If only he could just go to sleep forever; if only he could die. But perhaps that *'sleep of death'* would be like his sleep ever since his father died: full of terrible dreams.

'For in that sleep of death what dreams may come
When we have shuffled off this mortal coil,
Must give us pause.'

What should he do?

Ophelia greets Hamlet. She says she has some gifts that Hamlet has given her in the past. Now she wants to return them. Hamlet tells her that can't be so, because he knows he's never given her anything.

They talk. Hamlet tells Ophelia, *'I did love you once,'* but then he tells her, *'You should not have believed me … I loved you not.'*

No matter how hard we all try to be good, Hamlet continues, our sins come out in the end. We are all sinners. *'Get thee to a nunnery. Why wouldst thou be a breeder of sinners?'* he tells Ophelia. (In a nunnery, she would not be able to have any children.)

He tells Ophelia that if she marries, she will get a bad reputation. It doesn't matter how well she behaves. She is like his mother, like all women: she paints on one face and underneath there is another, quite different.

He tells her again, '*Get thee to a nunnery.*' Then he leaves.

Is Hamlet mad? Or is he pretending to be mad? Or is he just very distressed? Ophelia has no doubt that he is mad: '*O, what a noble mind is here o'erthrown!*'

With Hamlet gone, Claudius and Polonius come out of hiding. Claudius thinks that Hamlet is suffering from neither madness nor love, but Polonius says again that Hamlet is just in love (with his daughter).

They agree that, after the play, Gertrude will speak with Hamlet, and Polonius will secretly listen to their conversation. If Gertrude can't find the source of her son's madness, then Claudius will send Hamlet to England.

'Madness in important people must be closely watched,' says Claudius.

The court is getting together to watch the play. Hamlet has told the actors exactly what he wants them to do. He has also told Horatio of his plan, and tells him to watch the king closely during the scene, looking for signs of guilt.

The play starts with a mime to give the audience an idea of what the play is about. A king and a queen are very much in love. They embrace. The king lies down to sleep and a poisoner pours poison in his ear. The king dies and the queen is sad. The poisoner pretends sadness as well, but he brings her gifts. Then the queen goes off with the poisoner.

Then the actors begin the performance.

The play-queen protests undying love for the play-king. 'Only a woman who killed her first husband, would marry a second!' says the play-queen.

Hamlet asks Gertrude what she thinks of the play. *The lady* [play-queen] *protests too much, methinks,*' she says.

'Do you know the play, Hamlet? Is there any offence in the story?' Claudius asks.

'*No, no, they do but jest, poison in jest; no offence i' the world,*' replies Hamlet. 'But it doesn't matter. Your majesty and I have clear consciences, so we can watch without being bothered. Let the people who are guilty flinch.'

The play continues and, sure enough, when the poisoner pours the poison in the king's ear, Claudius stands up and rushes out. The courtiers and the queen run after him.

'Did you see that, Horatio?' Hamlet asks.

'*Very well, my lord,*' says Horatio grimly.

Rosencrantz and Guildenstern approach Hamlet. The king is very upset, and Gertrude has asked to see Hamlet in her rooms.

Hamlet agrees to go to see her soon, but first he tells Guildenstern, 'You are trying to play me like you play a pipe, but *you cannot play upon me.*'

Claudius is feeling his guilt. He has killed his brother – a terrible crime. '*O, my offence is rank it smells to heaven.*' He wants to pray, but his feelings of guilt are stronger.

He thinks about this guilt. He has got everything he wanted from his crime: he is king, and he has Gertrude. Is it possible he can be forgiven *and* keep the rewards of his crime? Not in Heaven, he can't; he is one of the damned. He knows this.

Just as Claudius kneels to pray, Hamlet enters and sees him there, on his knees. Now! Now he could do it! He could kill Claudius right now.

Hamlet draws his sword, then stops and thinks again. If he kills Claudius while he is praying, when his soul is purged, wouldn't Claudius go straight to Heaven?

Hamlet needs to wait until Claudius is doing something that has no trace of Heaven in it. So that when Claudius dies,

'*his soul may be as damn'd and black*
    As hell, whereto it goes.'

So Hamlet puts his sword away and goes
to see his mother.

In Queen Gertrude's room, Polonius is
hiding behind a hanging tapestry when
Hamlet enters. He will spy on Hamlet and
report back to Claudius.

'You have really offended your father,'
the queen tells Hamlet.

'*Mother, you have my father much offended,*'
Hamlet replies. 'Now sit down! You need to

take a good look at how you've been behaving.'

'Will you murder me?' Gertrude asks. 'Help! Help!' Is she afraid of her son?

Behind the tapestry, Polonius hears her calls for help – and he too shouts, 'Help!'

Hearing the shout, Hamlet thrusts his sword through the tapestry, shouting '*How now! a rat?*' – and kills Polonius.

'What have you done?' Gertrude screams, as Hamlet pulls the tapestry aside and sees Polonius lying dead. Hamlet speaks to him:

Thou wretched, rash, intruding fool, farewell!

I took thee for thy better.' (Hamlet thought it was Claudius hiding behind the tapestry.)

'What have you done?' Hamlet yells at his mother. 'My father was like a god. Look at Claudius! He is like a rotten ear of corn, infecting the one next to it. You can't even say it was the heat of passion. You are too old for that! What was it that blinded you?'

'O, *speak to me no more;*' replies Gertrude. '*These words, like daggers, enter in mine ears.*'

Then, in Gertrude's room, the ghost suddenly appears once more – but this time only Hamlet can see it.

'What do you want?' Hamlet asks the ghost.

'Take care of her, Hamlet, she is weak,' the ghost tells him. Then it disappears.

'Are you mad, Hamlet?' Gertrude asks. 'Who were you speaking to?'

'Oh no,' Hamlet tells Gertrude. 'Don't soothe your soul by thinking that it's my madness rather than your crime. You must repent and confess your sins. And don't ever tell the king that I'm not really mad, but only pretending.

'Now, I have to go to England with *my two schoolfellows* Rosencrantz and Guildenstern, who I trust just as much as I trust fanged snakes. I know their game and I'm watching them, so don't worry about me. *Good night, mother.*'

Hamlet leaves, dragging Polonius's dead body behind him.

FOUR

King Claudius has decided that Hamlet must be sent away to England *'for thine especial safety'*, accompanied by the courtiers Rosencrantz and Guildenstern.

Claudius hands the two courtiers a letter to give to the King of England. The letter asks the English king to have Hamlet killed in England. This is Claudius's plan.

Meanwhile, the fair Ophelia has already lost her true love, Hamlet. And she has lost her father, killed by Hamlet. Now she has lost her mind! She roams the countryside outside the castle, picking bundles of wild flowers, singing and talking nonsense.

Laertes, her brother, has already returned from France to Denmark, to avenge his father's death. Why, he asks Claudius, was Polonius buried secretly in an unmarked grave? And who killed him?

'None of this is my fault!' Claudius tells Laertes. 'I will help you find the guilty man. *And where the offence is let the great axe fall.*' We know who Claudius is thinking about!

Meanwhile, Horatio receives some letters, delivered to him in Elsinore by some sailors. One letter is from Hamlet, who is now back in Denmark. On the ship to England, the letter says, Hamlet was taken prisoner by pirates. Horatio is to give the enclosed letters to King Claudius and Queen Gertrude, and then come with the sailors to meet Hamlet. '*I have words to speak in thine ear will make thee dumb*,' Hamlet writes in the letter.

The letters are given to the king and queen. In his letter to Claudius, Hamlet tells him that he (Hamlet) is back in Denmark and he will meet the king tomorrow.

Claudius immediately tells Laertes that he shall have the opportunity to kill Hamlet, his father's murderer. Together they plot Hamlet's death.

Laertes is an ace swordsman and he will tip his sword with deadly poison. In addition, Claudius will poison a goblet of wine and offer it to Hamlet. So if Laertes fails to kill him, they will have a second chance.

As they talk, Gertrude enters with news for Laertes: his sister, Ophelia, is dead. She was wandering along the riverbank outside the castle, picking flowers. The branch of a particular willow tree, overhanging the river, caught her eye. She climbed out on it and the branch cracked. Ophelia fell into the freezing water. At first she floated and happily sang as she moved along. But she grew colder and her clothes took up water, until finally she drowned, sinking down to the muddy riverbed.

Laertes has no family left.

Hamlet and Horatio meet in a churchyard. Sadly, Hamlet watches the gravediggers larking about while they dig, scattering bones and digging up a skull, cracking jokes and laughing.

Hamlet has thought so much recently about death. He watched Fortinbras march his army across Denmark to fight in Poland. So many of those men would die, just for a bit of land!

One of the gravediggers shows Hamlet the skull of Yorick, the court jester, a man who, when Hamlet was a little boy, used to have the whole court roaring with laughter

with his juggling and acrobatics. Hamlet
even remembers riding on the man's back.

'*Alas, poor Yorick!
I knew him, Horatio:
a fellow of infinite
jest, of most excellent
fancy.*'

But then, this is
how everyone ends
up, even great
soldiers like Caesar
and Alexander the
Great.

The two men see a procession make its
way into the churchyard. King Claudius,
the queen, priests, mourners and Laertes
are taking somebody to their final rest.

Horatio and Hamlet hide and watch the
proceedings. It is Ophelia's funeral procession.

'I thought you would be Hamlet's bride,'
Gertrude sobs. 'I thought I would throw
flowers on your wedding bed, not on your
grave.'

Laertes is beside himself with grief. He jumps into Ophelia's grave, to hold her one last time.

Hamlet realises who they are burying. He steps forward and he too jumps into the grave. *'This is I, Hamlet the Dane!'* Something snaps inside his head. *'I loved Ophelia: forty thousand brothers*

Could not with all their quantity of love,
Make up my sum.'

Laertes takes Hamlet by the throat. He is overcome with anger and the courtiers have to stop them fighting, then and there, in the open grave. They force them apart and Hamlet storms off with Horatio.

Claudius reminds Laertes of their plan to deal with Hamlet. 'All will be well,' he promises.

Back at the castle, Hamlet tells Horatio about everything that happened on his journey to England. On the ship, he says, he found a letter that Rosencrantz and Guildenstern were carrying. It was from Claudius to the King of England, asking him to have Hamlet killed.

Hamlet took that letter and replaced it with another letter that he wrote. The new letter asked the King of England to kill the bearers of this letter, straight away, no questions asked. Hamlet then put the new letter amongst Rosencrantz and Guildenstern's papers. Now the two courtiers are dead.

Horatio says he is amazed at what Claudius has done. Hamlet is bitter. 'He has killed my father and slept with my mother. He has stolen my crown. I am going to kill him.'

'Then do it quickly, before he learns about what happened in England.'

'A man's life can be taken very quickly,' says Hamlet.

Hamlet tells Horatio he is sorry he lost his temper with Laertes in the churchyard. Laertes has lost his sister and his father.

Hamlet makes up his mind to try to tell Laertes of his guilt and regret.

As they talk, a young courtier, **Osric**, arrives with a message from the king. He tells them that Claudius has bet six horses, six swords and three carriages that in twelve bouts of fencing, Laertes will not hit Hamlet three times more than Hamlet hits Laertes.

Hamlet knows Laertes is a good swordsman, but he agrees to the duel. He has been practising, and anyway, to be honest, he might just be past caring.

With everybody watching, Hamlet and Laertes prepare for the bout. Hamlet apologises to Laertes, blaming his madness for his behaviour. Laertes acts graciously. He knows he has a poisoned rapier and a poisoned goblet on his side, so it's no big deal.

'Come on, Laertes!' Hamlet puts up his sword and manages to hit Laertes almost at once.

'Let's drink to that!' Claudius says. 'I have put a pearl in the cup for you, Hamlet, if you drink deep!'

'No, let's keep going!' Hamlet hits Laertes again.

'Our son will win!' Claudius shouts. (What a creep!)

Suddenly Gertrude snatches up the poisoned goblet. Claudius sees her lift it to her lips and take a mighty drink from it.

The two men fight again. Laertes is impressed by Hamlet's courage and feels almost guilty.

'Come on,' says Hamlet. 'What are you waiting for?'

Then suddenly Hamlet is wounded by Laertes' poisoned blade. Hamlet drops his sword, and Laertes trips and drops his own sword too.

Hamlet bends to pick up his sword, but snatches up Laertes' sword by mistake. Before Laertes can shout out, Hamlet has wounded him with it.

Hamlet and Laertes stand there, facing each other, both with poisoned wounds.

Everybody thinks the queen is fainting at the sight of all the blood, but then she falls down stone dead.

Laertes is struggling for breath. '*I am justly kill'd with mine own treachery,*' he says.

He tells Hamlet they have both been stabbed with the poisoned sword. '*Hamlet, thou art slain;*

No medicine in the world can do thee good.'

Then Laertes tells Hamlet, '*The king, the king's to blame.*'

Hamlet knows he does not have long to live. He stabs Claudius with the poisoned sword and, as Claudius dies, Hamlet forces him to drink the poisoned wine.

At last he has kept his promise!

Then Laertes dies, saying:

'*Exchange forgiveness with me, noble Hamlet:*

Mine and my father's death come not upon thee,

Nor thine on me.'

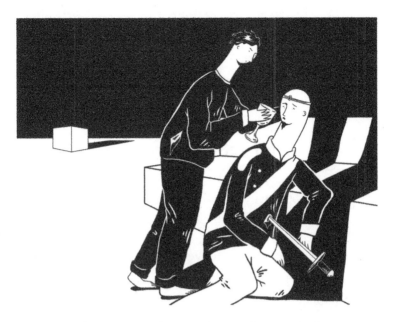

Hamlet too is dying. He takes another sip of the poisoned wine, then names Young Fortinbras as the next king of Denmark. Then Hamlet dies.

Horatio is heartbroken.

'Good night sweet prince:
And flights of angels sing thee to thy rest!'

 **THE END**

What's the play about?

This is probably Shakespeare's most famous play. It's also his most complex play.

After a quick read you'd probably be thinking that the play is mainly about **revenge**. Hamlet wants to get revenge on Claudius for killing his father, old King Hamlet.

But really revenge is only the starting point for other, more interesting themes that the play explores.

The play is also about how to live in a world that seems to be cruel and corrupt, where everybody seems to deceive each other.

In such a world, who can you trust? What can you trust? Did Claudius kill old

King Hamlet? Or is the ghost of the king an evil spirit?

Claudius and Polonius both send out spies (to spy on Hamlet and Laertes respectively). Claudius asks the king of England to kill Hamlet, then, when that fails, he plots with Laertes to kill Hamlet.

Hamlet too deceives; he pretends to be mad – and the audience, as well as the characters in the play, can't be sure whether he really is mad or not.

The story of *Hamlet* is one that has been recreated in films, stories and plays around the world. Even the Disney film *The Lion King* is based on *Hamlet*.

What are the main themes in the play?

Revenge – Hamlet wants to get revenge against Claudius for killing his father, old King Hamlet.

Madness – After first meeting the ghost, Hamlet tells Horatio that he may be forced to act as if he were mad (or, as he says, '*put an antic disposition on*') in his bid to kill Claudius.

Later in the play, when Hamlet starts to act in a strange way, we naturally think that he is pretending to be mad. But it isn't really that clear. Sometimes Hamlet seems to be acting, but other times it seems as if he really is mad. Which is it? Or is it both?

Actually, whether Hamlet is really going mad or not isn't the most interesting question. The real question is: why does Hamlet decide to fake madness to kill Claudius? Couldn't he just ... well, kill him?

Ophelia goes mad in the play, too. She loved Hamlet, but his behaviour towards her frightens her. She also suffers after the murder of her father. Is Shakespeare showing us the terrible effects of a corrupt world on an innocent person?

Death – Death and the fact that, in the end, we all die is possibly the main theme of the play. Death seems to be everywhere: eight of the nine main characters in the play die: old King Hamlet, Claudius, Polonius, Laertes, Ophelia, Rosenkrantz, Guildenstern and Hamlet himself.

Hamlet broods about death all the time. His famous '*To be or not to be*' speech is really about whether (and how) to carry on living in such a corrupt world.

It's only when Hamlet holds the court jester Yorick's skull, that he seems to realise that death eliminates the differences between people. In the end, everybody is eaten by worms, everybody crumbles into dust.

Corruption – Hamlet is surrounded by corruption. It's clear that King Claudius is corrupt and so is his court. At one point Claudius says, '*Oh, my offence is rank it smells to heaven.*' Claudius wonders if he can keep the benefits of his crime (becoming king and marrying Gertrude) and also go to Heaven after his death.

Families are corrupt too: Hamlet's uncle killed his father, and Ophelia struggles to please both her father and brother.

Hamlet's view of people is very dark. He tells Ophelia, '*Get thee to a nunnery: why wouldst thou be a breeder of sinners?*'

Deception – 'How can we be sure of anything?' is a constant theme in the play. How can Hamlet know that Claudius killed his father? Nobody saw him do it. Can Hamlet believe what the ghost tells him? Or is the ghost just an evil spirit?

Is Hamlet really mad – or is he just deceiving people? Claudius too is deceitful, sending spies to observe Hamlet and plotting to have him killed.

Sexuality – The play offers a very harsh view of women. Hamlet seems to link female sexuality with moral corruption. '*Frailty, thy name is woman!*' he says at one point.

Polonius tells his daughter Ophelia exactly how to behave with Hamlet, but he tells his son Laertes to be true to himself. There is one rule for men and another for women, it seems.

In fact, Ophelia is dominated by her brother and her father. Neither of them shows any interest in her true feelings.

Shakespeare's words

Language is very important in *Hamlet*. The characters deceive and manipulate each other throughout the play, and this is mainly done with words.

Sometimes Shakespeare uses **repetition** to make a point more strongly.

* ✳ When Polonius asks Hamlet what he reads, he replies '*Words, words, words.*' In Hamlet's (seeming) madness, everything is just words.

Shakespeare also uses **metaphors** and **similes**, comparing things in a way that helps us understand how the characters feel.

* Hamlet asks himself:
  'Whether 'tis nobler in the mind to suffer
  The slings and arrows of outrageous
  fortune,
  Or to take arms against a sea of troubles,
  And by opposing end them?

  He is comparing his troubles to an ocean, making us feel that they too are vast and endless, like the sea.

* When Hamlet says harsh things to his mother, Gertrude, she replies:
  'These words, like daggers, enter in mine ears.'

  In other words, Hamlet's words hurt her just as if they were daggers, hurting her body.

Sometimes Shakespeare wants us to know what his characters are **thinking**.

* Hamlet often talks to himself, with little speeches that nobody is meant to hear. (This kind of speech is called a

soliloquy.) It is a way of letting the audience know what the character is really thinking (and not just what he or she is saying to others).

In Hamlet's case this is very important for the audience, as it helps us to understand what is troubling him and how he sees the world. It also helps us judge whether he is really mad.

His famous speech that starts, '*To be, or not to be*,' is a soliloquy. Hamlet considers suicide, to put the misery of his life to an end, but he does not know what will happen to him after his death. The afterlife could be much worse than how things are now.

Which is why, in the end, he seems to decide just to carry on living.